Hidden disaster

ERIK BONGERS

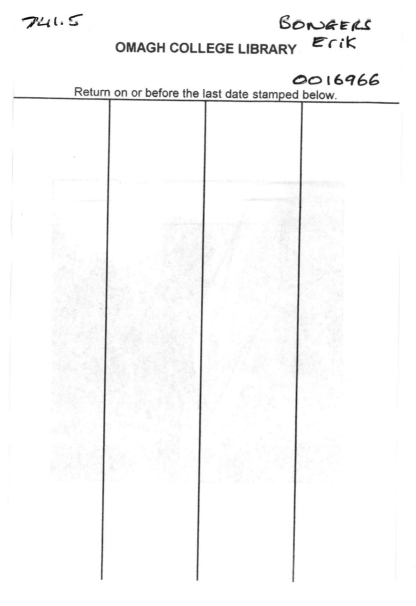

Special thanks to Thorsten Münch for his vital input to the story.
Special thanks to Alexandre Istratov for allowing the use of his photographic vistas of Brussels.
http://www.istratov.be

"Hidden disaster" is a wholly fictitious story written to illustrate how the European Commission's Humanitarian
Aid department responds to crises, from a human interest angle. Any resemblance to real people is entirely
coincidental.

**Europe Direct is a service to help you find answers
to your questions about the European Union**

Freephone number (*):

00 800 6 7 8 9 10 11

(*) Certain mobile telephone operators do not allow access to 00 800 numbers or these calls may
be billed.

More information on the European Union is available on the Internet: http://europa.eu

For information about the European Commission's humanitarian aid, see: http://ec.europa.eu/echo

Cataloguing data can be found at the end of this publication.

Luxembourg: Publications Office of the European Union, 2010

KR-31-09-144-EN-C
ISBN: 978-92-79-13380-0
doi: 10.2795/11166

Printed in Germany

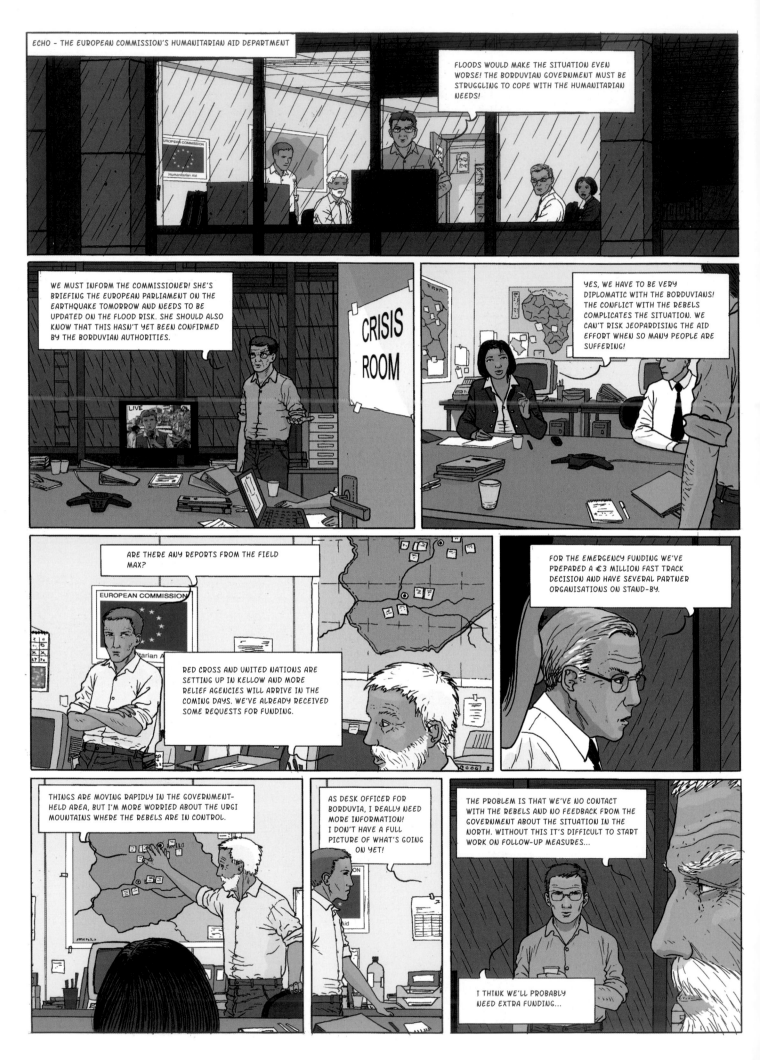

ECHO - THE EUROPEAN COMMISSION'S HUMANITARIAN AID DEPARTMENT

FLOODS WOULD MAKE THE SITUATION EVEN WORSE! THE BORDUVIAN GOVERNMENT MUST BE STRUGGLING TO COPE WITH THE HUMANITARIAN NEEDS!

WE MUST INFORM THE COMMISSIONER! SHE'S BRIEFING THE EUROPEAN PARLIAMENT ON THE EARTHQUAKE TOMORROW AND NEEDS TO BE UPDATED ON THE FLOOD RISK. SHE SHOULD ALSO KNOW THAT THIS HASN'T YET BEEN CONFIRMED BY THE BORDUVIAN AUTHORITIES.

CRISIS ROOM

YES, WE HAVE TO BE VERY DIPLOMATIC WITH THE BORDUVIANS! THE CONFLICT WITH THE REBELS COMPLICATES THE SITUATION. WE CAN'T RISK JEOPARDISING THE AID EFFORT WHEN SO MANY PEOPLE ARE SUFFERING!

ARE THERE ANY REPORTS FROM THE FIELD MAX?

EUROPEAN COMMISSION

FOR THE EMERGENCY FUNDING WE'VE PREPARED A €3 MILLION FAST TRACK DECISION AND HAVE SEVERAL PARTNER ORGANISATIONS ON STAND-BY.

RED CROSS AND UNITED NATIONS ARE SETTING UP IN KELLOW AND MORE RELIEF AGENCIES WILL ARRIVE IN THE COMING DAYS. WE'VE ALREADY RECEIVED SOME REQUESTS FOR FUNDING.

THINGS ARE MOVING RAPIDLY IN THE GOVERNMENT-HELD AREA, BUT I'M MORE WORRIED ABOUT THE URGI MOUNTAINS WHERE THE REBELS ARE IN CONTROL.

AS DESK OFFICER FOR BORDUVIA, I REALLY NEED MORE INFORMATION! I DON'T HAVE A FULL PICTURE OF WHAT'S GOING ON YET!

THE PROBLEM IS THAT WE'VE NO CONTACT WITH THE REBELS AND NO FEEDBACK FROM THE GOVERNMENT ABOUT THE SITUATION IN THE NORTH. WITHOUT THIS IT'S DIFFICULT TO START WORK ON FOLLOW-UP MEASURES...

I THINK WE'LL PROBABLY NEED EXTRA FUNDING...

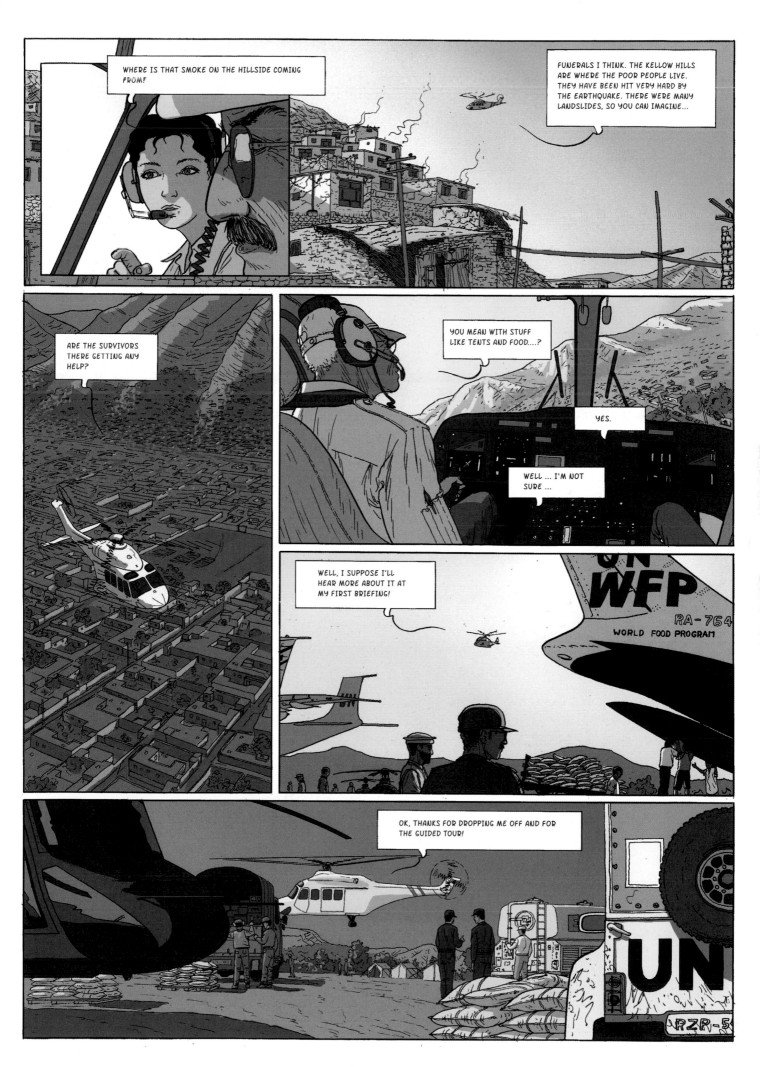

DAY 5.

KELLOW, UNITED NATIONS BASE CAMP

GOOD MORNING, EVERYONE!

WELCOME TO TODAY'S BRIEFING. FIRST I WANT TO WELCOME AND INTRODUCE ZANA TO THE TEAM.

ZANA IS AN ECHO FIELD EXPERT - FROM THE EUROPEAN COMMISSION. SHE'S HERE TO ASSESS THE SITUATION IN THE URGI MOUNTAINS. THE INFORMATION SHE OBTAINS WILL BE VITAL TO EXPANDING OUR EFFORTS IN THAT AREA...

WHILE WE WAIT FOR HER TRAVEL PERMITS TO ARRIVE, ZANA WILL BE WORKING WITH THE TEAM HERE.

OK, STATUS REPORT THEN...

OUR CURRENT ESTIMATE IS 20,000 DEAD AND I'M SORRY TO SAY THE COUNT IS RAPIDLY RISING! ABOUT 30,000 ARE INJURED...

WITH MORE AND MORE AID ORGANISATIONS ARRIVING, IT'S IMPORTANT WE USE THESE MORNING MEETINGS TO COORDINATE OUR EFFORTS. I'D LIKE A REGULAR UPDATE FROM EVERY ORGANISATION PRESENT HERE!

WE'RE TREATING PEOPLE WITH VARIOUS WOUNDS IN THE RED CROSS FIELD HOSPITAL. BUT THERE ARE A LOT OF EMPTY BEDS. SOMETHING IS PREVENTING INJURED PEOPLE REACHING US.

IT COULD BE BECAUSE THE ROADS ARE BLOCKED OR BECAUSE THEY SIMPLY DON'T KNOW ABOUT THE FIELD HOSPITAL.

ASSESSMENT OF INFORMAL CAMP IN KELLOW FOR DISPLACED PEOPLE. ENTRY AND REGISTRATION OF NEW ARRIVALS WELL-ORGANISED BY THE LOCAL AUTHORITIES.

THE CAMP RELIES ON LARGE STORAGE BLADDERS FOR ITS WATER SUPPLY. THERE ARE ENOUGH OF THESE, BUT CHILDREN ARE PLAYING ON TOP OF THEM AND THEY ARE LIKELY TO GET DAMAGED. THEY NEED TO BE ENCLOSED FOR PROTECTION.

YES, YES, I KNOW YOU'RE HAVING FUN BUT WHAT IF YOU BURST THE TANK? WE NEED THE WATER FOR DRINKING, COOKING AND WASHING!

THE TENTS ARE POORLY SITED: THE ARRANGEMENTS ARE TOO CHAOTIC AND IMPRACTICAL IF THE CAMP IS TO BE HERE FOR A LONG TIME.

THESE TENTS ARE MUCH TOO CLOSE TOGETHER! YOU CAN HARDLY WALK BETWEEN THEM! IT MAY BE A MINOR DETAIL BUT THEY COULD HAVE BEEN PITCHED IN A WAY THAT GIVES THE FAMILIES MORE PRIVACY!

TESJANG, IS IT OK IF WE DO SOME INTERVIEWS NOW?

...AND HE SAYS THAT HE ONLY RECEIVED ONE TENT. BUT HE HAS A LARGE FAMILY AND ONE IS NOT ENOUGH...

HE COMPLAINS ABOUT UNFAIR FOOD DISTRIBUTION. HE IS ONLY ALLOWED ONE BAG. OTHER FAMILIES HAVE OLDER SONS THAT MANAGE TO GET EXTRA BAGS. SO THEY HAVE TWO OR THREE PER FAMILY!

HE SLEEPS IN THIS SMALL PLASTIC SHELTER. HE SAYS HIS NEIGHBOURS HAVE RECEIVED A LARGER TENT FOR A SMALLER FAMILY!

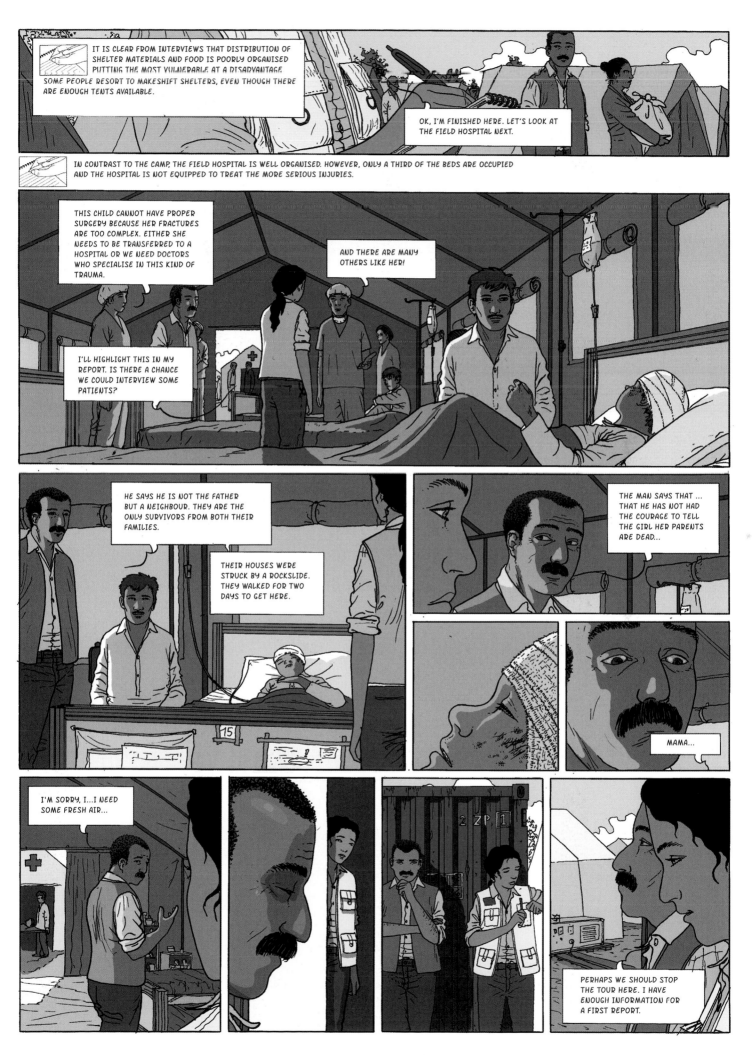

CONCLUSION OF SECTORAL ASSESSMENT OF THE KELLOW HILL AREAS. MOST HOUSES ARE UNINHABITABLE. NOTHING HAS BEEN DONE YET TO EVACUATE THE PEOPLE TO RELIEF CAMPS.

THE IMPACT OF THE EARTHQUAKE IS FAR WORSE IN THE HILLS THAN IN THE VALLEY.

LANDSLIDES SWEPT AWAY ENTIRE NEIGHBOURHOODS IN JUST A FEW SECONDS....

IT IS A SCENE OF UTTER DEVASTATION!

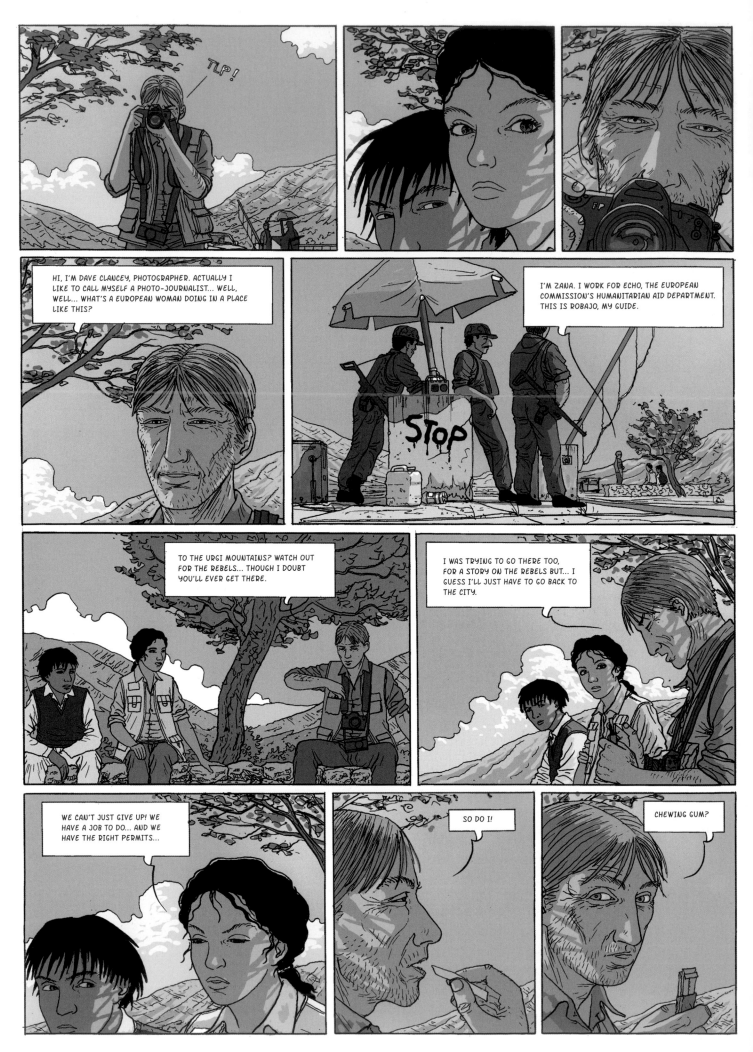

29

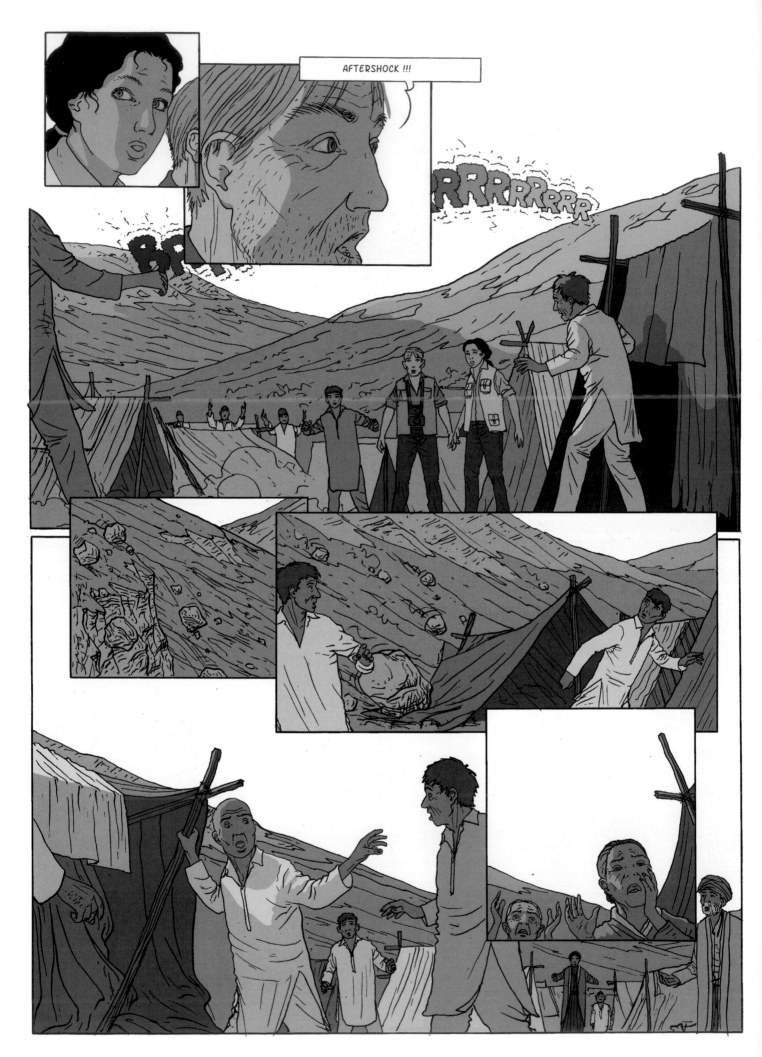

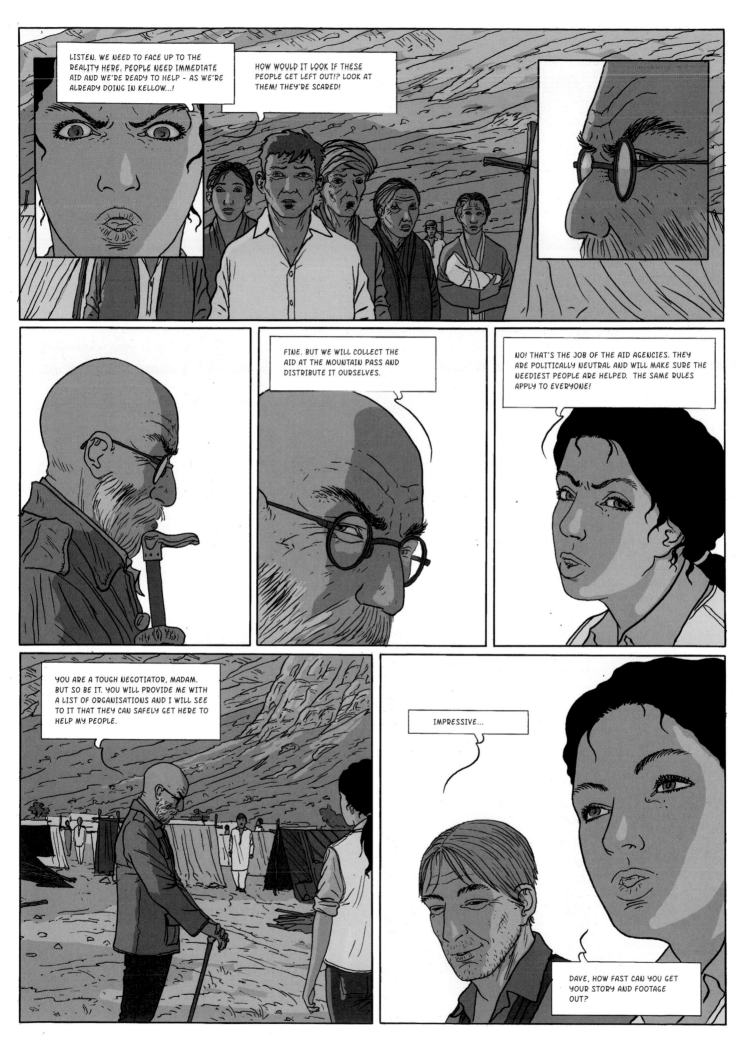

35

THREE MONTHS LATER...

IT'S GOOD TO SEE HOW SO MANY PEOPLE FROM THE FLOODED VALLEYS WERE GIVEN SHELTER.

THEY SHARED WHAT LITTLE THEY HAD. BUT THE HUMANITARIAN AID WAS VITAL IN THOSE DARK DAYS AFTER THE QUAKE STRUCK. AND NOW, WITH THESE NEW PUMPS, THEY HAVE CLEAN WATER...

ZANA... YOU KNOW THAT MANY BORDUVIANS WERE KILLED AND INJURED IN THE DISASTER. IT WILL TAKE A LONG TIME FOR THE PAIN TO GO AWAY... BUT...

I DON'T KNOW HOW TO PUT THIS... PEOPLE LIKE YOU HAVE REALLY HELPED TO RESTORE HOPE...

YOU'RE MAKING ME BLUSH!

WHAT ABOUT ALL THE WORK YOUR ORGANISATION PUT IN TOO. YOU WENT FOR DAYS WITHOUT SLEEP TO GET DRINKING WATER TO THE REMOTE VILLAGES...

GO ON! ... GIVE IT TO HER!

THE CHILDREN IN MY GRANDFATHER'S CLASS HAVE A GIFT FOR YOU. THEY HAVE MADE ALL THE ITEMS IN THIS BOX THEMSELVES. IT IS A TOKEN OF THEIR APPRECIATION. THEY WANT YOU TO TAKE IT BACK AND SHOW IT TO ALL THE OTHER PEOPLE WHO HELPED US.

EVERY YEAR, EVENTS SUCH AS CONFLICTS, DROUGHTS, EARTHQUAKES AND FLOODS TRIGGER HUMANITARIAN CRISES IN DIFFERENT PARTS OF THE WORLD. EVERY YEAR, MILLIONS OF PEOPLE FIND THEMSELVES WITHOUT SHELTER, FOOD, WATER OR MEDICAL CARE.

HELPING THE WORLD'S MOST VULNERABLE POPULATIONS IS A MORAL IMPERATIVE FOR THE INTERNATIONAL COMMUNITY. WHEREVER THE CRISIS MAY OCCUR AND WHATEVER THE TYPE OF INTERVENTION REQUIRED, HUMAN AND PHYSICAL RESOURCES NEED TO BE RAPIDLY MOBILISED TO MEET THE VICTIMS' VITAL NEEDS WHILE PRESERVING THEIR DIGNITY.

THE CAUSES OF HUMANITARIAN CRISES ARE MANY AND VARIED. THEY ARE OFTEN THE TRAGIC BY-PRODUCTS OF CONFLICT OR THE RESULT OF EXTREME WEATHER CONDITIONS. SOMETIMES NATIONAL ECONOMIC MISMANAGEMENT MAKES THE POOR DESTITUTE AND TURNS HUNGER INTO FAMINE.

WHETHER THEIR CAUSES ARE NATURAL OR MAN-MADE, SUCH CRISES INVARIABLY BRING GREAT HUMAN SUFFERING.

THE EUROPEAN COMMISSION HAS A LONGSTANDING COMMITMENT TO HELP THE VICTIMS OF SUCH CRISES. ITS HUMANITARIAN AID DEPARTMENT (ECHO) PROVIDES RELIEF ASSISTANCE THAT GOES DIRECTLY TO PEOPLE IN DISTRESS, IRRESPECTIVE OF THEIR NATIONALITY, RELIGION, GENDER, ETHNIC ORIGIN OR POLITICAL AFFILIATION. WORKING WITH ITS PARTNERS IN THE FIELD, ECHO ACTS SWIFTLY TO SUPPLY AID WHEN DISASTER STRIKES AND CONTINUES TO HELP STRICKEN REGIONS EVEN AFTER THE MEDIA SPOTLIGHT AND POLITICAL INTEREST HAS SHIFTED ELSEWHERE.

THE END

At a glance

Humanitarian crises

Humanitarian crises include both natural disasters and conflicts. The majority of crisis victims are civilians, with vulnerable communities in developing countries likely to suffer most. Displaced people and refugees, who have lost their homes and possessions, are particularly at risk. Providing aid to those who are most in need is a concrete expression of the universal value of solidarity.

Humanitarian actors

National authorities are responsible in the first instance for helping their people in a crisis. Sometimes, the scale of a disaster can be overwhelming, however, and this is when international solidarity is vital. The European Union is the world's largest humanitarian donor, with funds channelled through the Commission's Humanitarian Aid department (ECHO) as well bilateral support from individual EU countries. ECHO works with around 200 implementing partners: specialised United Nations agencies; the Red Cross/Crescent movement and non-governmental organisations (NGOs). The aid goes impartially to the affected populations, regardless of their race, ethnic group, religion, gender, age, nationality or political affiliation.

Humanitarian space

The situation in crisis zones is often chaotic. A "humanitarian space" is essential for the safe and secure delivery of relief assistance but, in many places, aid operations are hindered because of violence and insecurity. It is increasingly difficult for humanitarian agencies to reach out to people in desperate need.

International Humanitarian Law (IHL) exists to protect non-combatants and ensure the delivery of life saving aid in war zones. Those who attack the humanitarian space are breaking the law.

Humanitarian principles

The European Union has a strong commitment to uphold and promote the humanitarian principles. The respect for them is essential for humanitarian actors to be able to work on the ground.

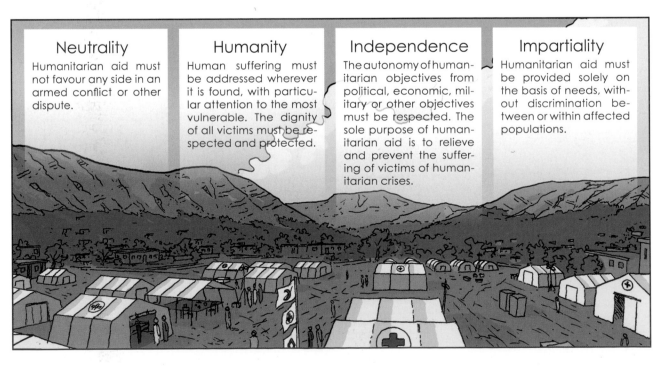

Neutrality
Humanitarian aid must not favour any side in an armed conflict or other dispute.

Humanity
Human suffering must be addressed wherever it is found, with particular attention to the most vulnerable. The dignity of all victims must be respected and protected.

Independence
The autonomy of humanitarian objectives from political, economic, military or other objectives must be respected. The sole purpose of humanitarian aid is to relieve and prevent the suffering of victims of humanitarian crises.

Impartiality
Humanitarian aid must be provided solely on the basis of needs, without discrimination between or within affected populations.

European Commission

Hidden Disaster

Luxembourg: Publications Office of the European Union

2010 — 40 pp. — 21 x 29,7 cm

KR-31-09-144-EN-C
ISBN: 978-92-79-13380-0
doi: 10.2795/11166